Golden Boy

and Other Stories from Burma

Golden Boy

and Other Stories from Burma

Saw Wai Lwin Moe
Edited by Irene Moilanen

White Lotus Press

White Lotus Co., Ltd.
G.P.O. Box 1141
Bangkok 10501
Thailand

Telephone: (662) 332-4915 and (662) 741-6288-9
Fax: (662) 741-6607 and (662) 741-6287
E-mail: ande@loxinfo.co.th
Website: http://thailine.com/lotus
Printed in Thailand

ISBN 974-7534-65-7 pbk White Lotus Co., Ltd., Bangkok

Cover art by Tuula Moilanen

Contents

Introduction vii

Legends

FRAGRANT RICE: Legend of the Creation of World 1

KING PYUSAWTHI: Legend of the First Burmese Kingdom 7

TWO BROTHERS: Legend of How the Peoples of Burma Divided 11

SHWEDAGON: Legend of the Great Golden Pagoda 13

GUARDIAN IN THE COCONUT: Legend of Maung Tin De 17

LEGEND OF THE TAUNGPYON BROTHERS 21

BAGO MEDAW: Legend of the Buffalo Mother 25

AUNGZWAMAGYI: Lord of the White Horse 29

LADY THON BAN HLA 33

Tales

THE HARP MASTER 37

THE WISE GIRL 41

RICH BOY DOES NOT LEARN 45

GOLDEN BOY 49

BEAUTIFUL BEYDAYI AND THE PRINCE 53

THREE SONS – THREE KYATS 57

FARMER AND ROBBERS 61

FATHER'S LOVE NEVER DIES 63

GOSSIPMONGER GETS HIS JUST DESERT 67

Fables

UNGRATEFUL SON 73

WHITE ELEPHANT AND THE HUNTER 79

THE HERMIT AND THE KEINNAYEE 83

RABBIT AS A FORTUNE TELLER 87

HUNTER SAVES THE VILLAGE 89

LITTLE RABBIT HAS A RUNNING NOSE 93

MANOUKTHIHA 95

THE MONKEY AND THE CROCODILE 99

RABBIT'S PICTURE IN THE MOON 101

Introduction

The following stories are just a tiny part of the world of fantastic legends, moral tales and exciting fables that surround the growing up of every Burmese child. There is always a grandmother, grandfather, aunt or uncle in the family who has time to entertain and educate the little ones. And what could be better and more soothing entertainment for a child, than the gentle voice guiding the little adventurer along the magic paths of the Golden Boy or brave and beautiful Ma Sabe.

These stories have been handed down through generations and time. They still convey the universal ideas of right and wrong, good and bad, as they have done for centuries. Shining devas, unpredictable nats, frightening balu demons, graceful keinnayees and wise yatheins live in the neighbourhood of the Burmese. The invisible spirit world is part of the national religion and culture. History and myth intertwine in many stories, where the mighty kings rule the destinies of the people. Many times the heroes and heroines are common villagers. In fables, the animal kingdom reflects human nature in humorous and apt ways.

The oral tradition lives on in the quiet farming villages, where the TV has not yet taken the place of the storyteller, but also in the modern cities. As long as there are myths and memories, there is genuine Burmese culture.

This small collection is divided into three parts. The first Legends reveal something of the mysteries of the history. The creation myth, the legends of the first king and some great heroes, provide the basis for who the Burmese are. The Tales inform us about the virtues, as do the Fables in the last section. In Fables we find animals sometimes behaving more like humans. All of the stories were told to the author of this book by loving family members, to pass the time or to educate him to meet the challenges of life. Some of the words and concepts possibly unfamiliar to the international reader are explained in a glossary at the end of this book.

This small collection of Burmese Legends, Tales and Fables is dedicated to the people and culture of the Golden Land.

Saw Wai Lwin Moe and Irene Moilanen

Legends

FRAGRANT RICE

Legend of the Creation of the World

There is no beginning or end to Time. The world is called *Loka*, which means it is created and destroyed in periods lasting far beyond human comprehension. This is the legend how life began in the human world as we know it.

In the beginning, the world was empty and quiet. There was only dry land and a vast sea. There was an island called *Zambhudipa* in the southern part of this world. A majestic mountain, *Myinmo*, rose in the middle of it, reaching up into the skies, right to the happy abodes of the d*eva nats*. One morning the rains came. First it rained slowly, but the wind blew strongly and it rained harder. Afterwards the sun shone on the wet land and formed a fertile cover. The surface of the world began to grow green grass, flowers and trees. Then, in the warmth of the sun, the trees blossomed and bore fruit. Insects, birds, animals and fish appeared to feed on nature's plentiful offerings.

By the effect of sun and water on the land a sweet butter-smelling nectar covered the open lands of the *Zambhudipa* island. The odour of this substance ascended up to the abodes of the d*eva nats*. The shining, translucent beings could not resist the sweet temptation. They assumed human bodies and flew down to taste the nectar. They ate happily to their heart's delight, and the more they ate, the more the surface produced the divine food. Soon the n*ats* became plump and lazy. Even though there was plenty of food for everyone, they became jealous and selfish and started to quarrel among themselves. As a punishment the *nats* lost their ability to fly and their bodies became dark and opaque. They were now human.

The nectar cover disappeared but a fragrant white rice took its place. The rice grew by itself and it was completely clean and huskless. The newly created mankind fed upon this new plant. They invented earthen vessels in which they cooked their rice. Different vegetables were added to the diet according to everyone's desire.

This new nourishment produced the first sensations of passion. Mankind divided into men and women, who fell in love with each other. Marriage was accepted as the way for humans to live, and the family the way to take care of their offspring. But these people too became jealous and envied their neighbours for their success and happiness. Because of these dark feelings, the rice stopped growing by itself. A lot of work was now needed to make the fields grow. People moved into villages and cities so they could do this work together. Each family had their piece of land where they built their house and kept their animals. Everyone, young and old, had to work hard in the field.

One moonless night a man went to his neighbour's field and cut some rice. In the morning this theft, the first crime, was noticed. People were very alarmed about this, so they elected a king among themselves, to administer justice and bestow rewards and punishment as deserved. He divided people into different professions. His sons became the royal race. Those who preserved their celibacy and remained unmarried became the Brahmins. The rest of the people became farmers, merchants, artisans and others. All tried to achieve happiness and live a good life.

This is how the world and all its creatures were born, and how they became what they are today. And this is how they will be until the great Wheel of Time turns and fire, water and wind destroy the world, reducing it to elements. In time the elements will again form a divine fertile cover on earth from which a new world will emerge.

KING PYUSAWTHI
Legend of the First Burmese Kingdom

Long, long ago, when the royal city of Pagan was but a small village, a n*aga* or snake princess called Zanthi lived in her father's underground kingdom. Princess Zanthi asked her father's permission to take human form and live in the world to practise the duties of virtue for her *kan*. She took a mountain near the villages of Mali as her home and lived there in peace and meditation.

Early one morning Princess Zanthi heard loud noises from the forest below. A handsome prince from the Surayavamsa family rode with his men up towards the mountain top where Zanthi was living. His face was shining like a sun and Zanthi fell in love with him at that very moment. When the prince saw the gentle and shy princess he thought: "This must be the most beautiful creature I have ever seen. I will make her my wife." The prince ordered his men to build a camp then and there. He took her hand and promised to love her always.

After a few happy days on the mountain top the prince became restless. He promised Zanthi to have her sent to the palace and told her to wait for his message. Then he went on his way, and forgot about the beautiful Zanthi. The princess waited and waited, but no messenger was to be seen approaching the mountain. Time went on and the deserted princess noticed that she was pregnant. When she was about to give birth, she sent a message to the prince that his heir was arriving in this world. The messenger, a white crow, was ordered not to come back without the prince's reply.

The prince was overjoyed on hearing the message. He wrapped a ruby ring in a silk cloth and sent the white crow back to carry the message to Zanthi. On the way from the Royal City the crow flew over a harbour, where merchants from different countries came and went on their business. It happened to be meal time, and the crow, as is the nature of crows, thought to pick up morsels of food. It left the ruby bundle in the fork of a tree. While the crow was picking up his food under the tables and benches, one of the merchants found the bundle. When he saw its valuable contents, he could not resist stealing the ring, and instead put a bundle of dry dung in its place. The dishonest merchant sailed to his country with the ring, but the crow flew back to Zanthi with the bundle. When the princess opened the silken message and found dung in it, her heart was broken. She took on her natural snake form, laid three eggs in a little cave under the shadow of a huge tree, and returned back to her father's kingdom.

Soon after Zanthi had left this world, a hunter happened to pass the same spot. While resting in the shade of the tree after the tiresome climb to the mountain top, his eye detected a golden glint from underground in the cave. He reached out for what he thought to be a hidden treasure, but found the three eggs instead. One of the eggs was white like the marble of Sagaing hills, one was shining black like the best lacquerware from Monywa and one was of purest gold. This finding surprised the hunter, but he guessed that such eggs had to be very valuable. Joyfully he carried the eggs in his backpack down the mountain. On the way to his home village he came to the riverbank of the Irrawaddy. He crossed the stream safely, but when he was about to climb to the shore, he slipped and dropped his valuable cargo into the water. Helplessly he watched the eggs floating swiftly down stream.

The golden egg broke in Mogok and changed into a thousand rubies, which can still be found in its ground. The black egg travelled until Thintwé. There, on shore, from an unbroken egg a beautiful girl was born. Later she became the Queen of Thintwé. Finally the white egg landed safely on the sandy shore in Nyaung-Oo. An old couple from a village near Pagan found the egg and took it to a hermit for advice. The hermit, being a man of wisdom and merit, prophesied: "This is not an ordinary egg. He who will be hatched out of it, will have glory, wisdom and the signs of royalty." The old couple, who did not have children of their own, were happy and treasured the egg with great care. In due time a little boy was born out of the egg. As the hermit had predicted, he had all the signs of royalty. His foster parents named him Pyusawthi. He was gentle and wise and respected the old couple as his parents.

In the meantime the prince from the family of the great Surayavamsa, the father of Pyusawthi, had been looking for Zanthi and her son. Regretting deeply his unfaithfulness to the princess he made a solemn vow to find his heir. The *nats* of the mountain felt pity on him, and told him where to look for his lost son. After many years, when the prince had already became king, he finally found Pyusawthi in the village of Nyaung-Oo living with his adopted parents. The king told his son about his real mother and gave him a magical golden bow and arrow, a present from the King of the *Nats* Thagya Min himself. "With these, my beloved son, you will be invincible, and found the greatest kingdom in this world." Then both the father and the son went to the garden where there were many *naga* holes in the ground, and left a present of milk and flowers to Zanthi, the *naga* princess.

From that day on people have been praying and making offerings to the *naga*, whenever they desire a gift of son in the family. But Pyusawthi grew strong and wise. There was no one braver than he was. Later, after many adventures, he became the king of all the land and founded the great kingdom of Pagan.

TWO BROTHERS

Legend of How the Peoples of Burma Divided

Long long ago, all the peoples of Burma lived together like a big family. The Burman and the Chin were brothers. They lived happily with their families near the river Irrawaddy. One morning the Chin wanted to go fishing. He went to the Burman´s house and asked to have his fishhook for the day. Of course the Burman lent him his fishhook, and the Chin went along to the riverbank.

It was a beautiful clear morning and the fish seemed to be hungry. The Chin caught many, but lastly a huge catfish swallowed the hook. He fought back so hard that the line broke. The catfish disappeared back in the deep with the hook inside it´s belly.

The Chin went back to his brother the Burman and explained how he had lost the hook. The Burman became very angry and insisted he wanted to have the hook back. The Chin went at once to the blacksmith and bought a shining new hook for his brother. But the Burman threw the new hook to the ground and said: "The old hook was a valuable heirloom. I want it back and no substitute will do!" "But how can I bring back the hook that the catfish swallowed?" asked the Chin helplessly. "Well, that is your problem!", replied the Burman without mercy.

Now the Chin also became angry. He took his sons, uncles and cousins and built a dam in the river. Then he fished all the fish up from the river, and finally caught the big old catfish. He cut it open, and found the lost hook there. Then he returned it to his Burman brother, and peace returned to the village.

A few weeks later, the Burman wanted to fry special rice for a celebration. He needed a huge frying pot, which he borrowed from his brother the Chin. The Chin lent him his clay frying pot. The Burman went back to his kitchen, and just as he was about to step inside, he stumbled and down he flew with the clay frying pot in his hand. Naturally, the pot broke into a thousand pieces!

The Burman went back to his brother´s house and apologised the accident. This time the Chin was merciless: "That frying pot was a valuable heirloom. I want it back and no substitute will do!", he shouted angrily. "But how can I repair the clay frying pot? It broke into a thousand pieces!", asked the Burman helplessly. "Well, that is your problem!" replied the Chin.

This silly quarrel divided the families of the two brothers, the Burman and the Chin. The Burman took his family and went down to the Irrawaddy plains. The Chin in turn led his family to the mountains. And that is where each pair of them still live.

SHWEDAGON

Legend of the Great Golden Pagoda

If you travel to Burma, you will certainly visit the most famous of Buddhist shrines in the world, the magnificent Shwedagon the Great Golden Pagoda in Rangoon. The history of Shwedagon intertwines with the early history of the Buddhist religion in Burma.

At the time when Gotama Buddha lived and taught in India, two merchants, Taphussa and Bhallika, lived in Suvannabhumi, the Golden Land. They were seasoned tradesmen and one day they set sail from Okkala towards the shores of India. They sailed several days and once safely there, they packed their goods on bullock carts and headed to the city of Benares.

One morning, just before noon, when the party was passing a verdant garden, the bullock carts suddenly stopped. The merchants and the drivers were surprised. The animals had rested well the previous night and had been given plenty of fresh drink the same morning. Now, they just refused to budge. Taphussa and Bhallika did not know that the bullocks had been made to stop here by King of the *Deva Nats*, Thagya Min, who was the guardian of their homeland.

Puzzled, the two merchants looked around for a shady place to rest while the drivers gave the animals some water in an attempt to make them continue. They saw a huge Bodhi tree growing in the garden. Underneath a man was sitting. He seemed to be deep in meditation, but a strange shimmering light surrounded his body.

Carefully and silently Taphussa and Bhallika came closer, as they did not want to disturb the sage. When they were quite near, he suddenly opened his eyes and asked where the two men had come from. His eyes were deep and full of inner wisdom, his voice was gentle and kind. Taphussa and Bhallika introduced themselves and asked if they could donate a humble present of honey cakes. The sage, who was none other than Gotama Buddha himself, accepted the offering. He then taught them the Four Noble Truths and the Eightfold Path, as well as the five precepts for lay people. Hearing all this, the two merchants from the city of Okkala in Suvannabhumi bowed to the ground respectfully three times. They asked the sage to present them something that they could take back to their homeland and honour as a relic. Buddha combed his short curly hair with his right hand and gave them eight hairs from his head.

The merchants stored the sacred hair in a golden box and treasured it for the rest of their journey in India. On their way back to the boats, they happened to pass through a small kingdom ruled by King Ajetta. This King had heard about the teachings of Buddha, but had never bothered to go and listen to him personally. On hearing that Taphussa and Bhallika, two foreign merchants, had managed to have such a valuable present from the famous sage, he became jealous. King Ajetta ordered the merchants to give him two of the precious hairs.

When the two merchants sailed back, there was a terrible storm at sea. The boat was thrown around by fierce winds and waves as if it was just a plain piece of dry wood. When the travellers had nearly hope, the King of *Nagas* raised his head above the waters, and promised to save the travellers in return for two of Buddha's sacred hair.

Arriving at Okkala the merchants Taphussa and Bhallika were greeted by King Okkalapa and hundreds of happy citizens. A grand festival was held in honour of the sacred relics. King Okkalapa announced that a pagoda would be built to enshrine the holy relics. The site chosen was Theinguttara hill. When the King's builders excavated the site of the future pagoda, they found the relics of three preceding Buddhas, namely a staff, a water-dipper and a lower garment. These were buried again together with the sacred hair. When the relics were examined before placing them in the vault, the golden box was miraculously found to contain the original number of eight hairs.

Thagya Min, the King of the *Deva Nats* participated in the building work with his entire court of d*eva nats*. Over the relic chamber a golden pagoda was erected. This in turn was enclosed in a silver pagoda, which was enclosed in tin, copper, lead, marble and iron pagodas. Finally a brick pagoda was built to encase the series of smaller pagodas.

Later Okkala became known as Dagon. Several kings enlarged, repaired and gilded the famous golden shrine of Dagon, the Shwedagon. Although a small town, Dagon was regarded as an important religious centre for Buddhists. Queen Shinsawbu (1453-1472) of Pegu, a devout Buddhist, built over the pagoda a still higher one, which is more or less the pagoda's present shape. She also gilded the pagoda from top to bottom for which she offered gold by her weight. In 1774 King Hsinbyushin of Ava put up a new *hti* – a jewelled ceremonial umbrella, and the pagoda attained its present height. The *hti* was replaced by yet another, even grander and more valuable, by King Mindon Min of Mandalay in 1871.

Burmese kingdom moved its capital several times during its long history, but Shwedagon has always been the most sacred of the thousands and thousands of pagodas scattered all around the Burmese landscape. King Alaungpaya united the Burmese kingdom in 1755. He renamed the small town of Dagon as Yangon, "End of Strife". The British colonial rulers tried to uncover the secrets of Shwedagon by excavating the great structure. These actions were considered as severe insult towards the religious feelings of the Burmese people and also as an attempt to destroy one of the most honoured symbols of Burmese culture. Fortunately the treasure hunt was unsuccessful and the damages done were rather small.

The sacred Great Golden Pagoda today reaches almost 100 meters in height. There are 64 small pagodas and four larger ones facing the cardinal points. A forest of *tazaungs*, wooden shrines with beautifully carved *pyatthat*-roofs, Buddhas of various sizes and materials and a multitude of sculpted images picturing the colourful and exciting world of Burmese myth and legends add to the fascinating and unique atmosphere of the place. Truly, a visit to Burma will be incomplete without visiting the magical Shwedagon, the grand symbol of what being Burmese is all about.

GUARDIAN IN THE COCONUT
Legend of Maung Tin De

Once upon a time there lived a strong and handsome blacksmith in the village of Tagaung. He was kind and helpful and much respected by his fellow men. The king heard stories praising Maung Tin De´s superior strength, and he became worried. Even though the *Shwepalin*, Golden Throne of the kings of Burma, and the undisputed power over the life and death of the people living in its shadow, is usually handed down from father to son, there are times in history when a usurper took his chance and seized power. If he is lucky, he will found a new dynasty as well as a new capital. So the king, learning about Maung Tin De´s popularity, was naturally afraid. "This blacksmith will rob me of my kingdom. Seize him and kill him!" ordered the king.

At once the soldiers rode to Tagaung village to look for Maung Tin De. Luckily for the blacksmith, he had a friend in the Royal Palace who had warned him about the king´s jealous hatred. So the blacksmith left his home and ran away to live in the jungle. His beautiful sister Shwe Myet Hna stayed behind to take care of the house.

When the king´s soldiers could not find Maung Tin De they took Shwe Myet Hna instead in front of the king for interrogation. But when the king saw Shwe Myet Hna´s delicate and frightened face, which shone as her name suggested, like pure gold, he felt his heart move. The king fell in love with the beauty, but he could not forget the fear he had for the brother. He made an evil plan to win both, the love and the fear. The king told Shwe Myet Hna not to be afraid, because he just wanted to meet such a mighty and famous man as her brother. He promised to make Maung Tin De a governor of a town and also to take Shwe Myet Hna as his queen, to love and cherish her always. Innocent Shwe Myet Hna believed the sweet lies of the monarch. On her wedding day she sent a word to her brother hiding in the jungle to come to the Royal Palace. Maung Tin De also trusted the king not to harm his wife's brother, but how mistaken he was! When the blacksmith stepped inside the gates of the Royal City, the king's soldiers attacked him and dragged him straightaway to the execution site. The poor blacksmith was tied to a tree and great pile of fuel was lit under his feet.

When Shwe Myet Hna heard her brother's shouts from the yard, she rushed down to find the horrible sight in front of her eyes. She realised the evil plan of the king and regretting ever having trusted him, jumped into the fire to die together with her beloved brother. "Because of me my brother had to die! I do not wish to live a day more!" she shouted as her last words. The king, who really had fallen for the gentle Shwe Myet Hna, tried to rescue his young queen from the flames. He clutched her hair and pulled her out, but it was too late. Only Shwe Myet Hna's beautiful golden face was saved.

The spirits of people who have suffered a violent death sometimes haunt the place where they met their sad fate. Maung Tin De and Shwe Myet Hna had turned into nats, who dwelled in a great tree growing in the yard of the Royal Palace. Any man, horse, buffalo or cow that wandered under the shadow of that tree, died. The king was now even more afraid of the angry nats than he had ever been of the blacksmith when he was alive. He ordered his men to dig up the tree and throw it into the Irrawaddy river.

The haunted tree together with the spirits living in it floated to the shores of the Royal City of Pagan. When mighty King Anawrahta heard about the sad fate of the brother and sister, he ordered the tree trunk cut into two, and images of the blacksmith and his faithful sister carved from it. The images were then taken to the holy mount Popa, where proper ceremonies were carried out to make peace with the nats. Also, Anawrahta nominated Maung Tin De as Min Mahagiri, the guardian of Burmese homes. To mark this he ordered that a coconut should be hung in honour of the spirit in the southeast corner of every Burmese house. If you have a chance to visit a Burmese home today, you will still find a coconut in a corner of the room.

LEGEND OF THE TAUNGPYON BROTHERS

There was a terrible storm one night, a long time ago, and a boat was wrecked near the shores of the kingdom of Arakan. Only two young men were saved. They struggled through the enormous waves until they reached the shore. Both of them fainted out of exhaustion and relief as soon as they felt firm ground under their feet.

Early next morning an old hermit happened to walk by on his way to collect some fruits in the forest. He spotted the men lying unconscious near the waterfront. The hermit pulled them one by one to his cabin, where the two brothers woke up in due course. He offered them food and shelter, which the brothers took with gratitude. The hermit asked them to stay until they had fully recovered their strength. The brothers gladly accepted this.

Days and weeks went by quietly. The hermit and the two brothers collected fruits and berries from the forest for their nourishment. One day as the young men wandered in the forest, they found a strange thing under a great old *pipal*-tree. It looked like a huge banana-bud, but it was empty inside, like a shell, and it smelled very fragrant and delicious. The two brothers decided to take this peculiar shell to the hermit. The hermit, on seeing the cover, knew at once that it was a magical shell belonging to a *zawgyi* magician, who had attained supernormal powers and flown away, leaving only this empty shell behind him. The man who ate this shell would become stronger than any man, almost invincible. The wise old hermit did not reveal his knowledge to his young and restless guests but decided to wait until they were maturer.

In the evening, as soon as the old hermit dosed off to sleep, the brothers started to whisper. "Hey brother, don't you feel hungry?" asked the younger one. "The sweet smell from that strange shell we found is making my appetite grow. Why don't we taste a bit," answered the older brother. And so the two brothers sneaked upto the shell and tasted it. So delicious was this magical food, that they ate it all. As soon as they had finished their muscles started to grow and their minds became full of wild ideas. The brothers rushed out into the dark night. They ran and ran without feeling tired until they arrived the king's city. There they at once got involved in trouble and fights. Nobody could stop them.

After some years of reckless life and many adventures the brothers decided to make better use of their power. The older one went down to the famous Mon city of Thaton to join the king's army. There he fell in love with one of the king's concubines. The lovers met in secret, but in the palace there are always jealous rivals and the king found out about the affair. He sent his soldiers to arrest the older brother, but in vain. No man was his match in battle and so the love affair went on under the jealous king's eyes. Finally, one of the ministers came up with an idea of how to catch the mighty warrior. The minister took one golden and red *longyi* belonging to the concubine, and hung it above the gate through which the older brother sneaked into the palace every night. Everyone knows that walking under a woman's lower garment makes a man weak and helpless, so the king's soldiers had an easy task to attack and kill the unsuspecting suitor there and then. His blood was spread on the walls of the palace to make them invincible – the older brother's spirit would protect the king's city forever.

In the meantime, the younger brother had travelled to the magnificent city of Pagan to serve as a general in King Anawrahta's army.

One day King Anawrahta sent his favourite general to Mount Popa to take charge of the flower offerings to the guardian nats of the Kingdom.

While walking in the forest, he heard somebody singing. He hid himself behind a tree and waited. A beautiful maiden dressed in bright green and golden *longyi* came singing along the path, picking wild roses as she walked. The general fell in love with her at the very first glimpse of her incomparable beauty. He stepped forward and revealed himself. The gentle maiden got scared when seeing the handsome general in the purple red uniform of the king´s army, but soon her heart was beating fast for him. The couple got married secretly and the general visited his wife as often as he could. What he did not realise was, that his wife was a flower-eating *bilu* ogress, who had taken a human form in order to practise virtues of compassion and charity for her merit.

In due time the *bilu* gave birth to two sons, which she named Shwebyin Naungdaw and Shwebyin Nyidaw. The boys inherited their father´s strength and handsome looks and their mother´s wild nature. When they grew up, they joined King Anawrahta´s troops, where they proved to be fearless heroes. The King soon noticed they were undisciplined and hot-headed, but he forgave them their manners many times because of their father the general, and for their services on the battlefield. The two brothers loved the company of beautiful maidens, and loud drinking parties, and you could be sure to find them where ever there was a cock-fight or gambling going on.

One day King Anawrahta decided to build a pagoda in the village of Taungpyon for his good merit. He ordered every villager, old and young, to work with his soldiers and generals; everyone had to bring one brick to the building site. Happy to join such an auspicious project each villager, soldier and officer carried their share to the construction site where the best masons of the kingdom were at work. Only Shwebyin Naungdaw and Shwebyin Nyidaw did not obey the order, being too busy throwing dice. When the mighty King Anawrahta found out about this insult to his authority and devotion of Buddhist religion, he ordered the two mischievous brothers to be executed at once. The two brothers became wild *nat*-spirits and were seen riding away on the back of a tiger. Their mother's heart was broken on hearing the news of her sons' fate, and she too fell down dead on her mountain slope.

From that day on the two *nat* brothers Shwebyin Naungdaw and Shwebyin Nyidaw have been giving trouble to people who don't respect them by offering a bottle of fierce Mandalay rum and a few *cheerots*. And even today, you can see the two bricks missing from the pagoda at Taungpyon.

BAGO MEDAW
Legend of the Buffalo Mother

Long ago, in the Kingdom of Pegu the royal princesses wished to go for a picnic in the orchid forest. The king gave his consent, so nine brilliantly decorated elephants were chosen from the king's stables to carry the party out from the walled city. There were nine princesses, their maids and twenty strong soldiers from the king's personal bodyguard. There was also a very young prince, the pride and joy of his father, who had begged permission to go, too.

It was a lovely day. In the cool shadows of the bamboo and huge jungle trees grew flowers of every colour. The royal party descended from their mounts and began to play, sing and pick the flowers. The little prince ran here and there. Everyone had fun. After lunch the princesses decided to have a short rest before riding back to the palace. The maids and soldiers also felt sleepy under the afternoon sun. Even the nine royal elephants fell asleep.

Only the little prince did not want to lie down. When he saw that nobody was about to play with him, he wandered a little further into the orchard forest. There he saw a huge green butterfly, as big as a sparrow and as shining as the emeralds in his father's bracelets. The little prince ran after the butterfly further and further into the forest until he found himself lost in the midst of bamboo bushes. He settled down tired from running around, sure that the princesses would come soon and take him home.

At the same time the oldest princess woke up. She looked for the little prince and when he was nowhere to be seen she called all the other princesses, the maids and soldiers. Everyone became afraid and worried. They called for the little prince, shouting his name, feeling all the time more and more anxious. When evening fell, and the little prince could not be found, they had to return to the Royal City, very much afraid of what the king would say.

Next morning the little prince woke up hungry and surprised. Where was his sister, the oldest princess, who always carried him so lovingly? Why were there no maids to bring him milk, and what happened to the soldiers, whose duty it was to guard his life? Annoyed he pushed the bamboo aside, only to tumble onto a big black lump, which seemed to be snoring. He hit the lump with his little fist and ordered it to move aside, because here came the prince. The lump lifted its head patiently, and only then did the prince see that it was a huge female buffalo. Now, some people think the tiger is the most dangerous animal in the jungle, but those who really know, will tell you it is the wild buffalo that you should be most afraid of. When a female buffalo is defending her young ones even a hungry tiger will retreat! But this buffalo was looking at the little prince, who now burst out crying out of fear, hunger and just feeling lonely. She felt a lot of pity for the boy, took him close to her and offered him her milk. After eating, he climbed on her back and they rode away.

The king sent search parties to look for the little prince as soon as dawn broke the next morning, but the only thing they could find was the little prince's pink *gaung baung* lying in the midst of the bamboo bush. The grieving king concluded that a tiger had eaten his son. He locked up in prison all the princesses, the maids and the soldiers who where on duty during the picnic that ended so sadly.

There they could not see the sun or the full moon rising over the Golden Palace.

Years passed and the little prince grew up nourished by his buffalo mother's milk, to become a handsome and strong youth. He learned how to make medicine from the plants and how to catch fish from the river with his bare hands. One afternoon, the king himself was riding on his white elephant in the forest. He saw a handsome youth, looking a little familiar, fishing near the riverside. He ordered his troops to stop and bring the youth in front of him. When the young man knelt down in front of him, the king recognised his long lost son. Joyfully they embraced each other and rode back to the royal city, where a big celebration began at once. All the princesses, maids and soldiers locked up in the prison were pardoned and the king ordered a *pwé*, grandest ever, to take place that night.

The buffalo mother, who had been taking her favourite mud bath when the king and prince found each other, was now desperate to find the prince whom she loved dearly. She followed the footsteps of the royal elephants and troops up to the mighty gates of the Royal City. The buffalo mother tried to push the gates open. She bellowed in great grief and tossed her horned head wildly. The guards at the gate were terrified. They sent a message to the palace about this strangely behaving buffalo, trying violently to make her way to the city. Only now did the prince remember his buffalo mother, who had taken tender care of him for so many years. He rushed to the gates of the city. When the buffalo mother saw her beloved son, she gathered all her strength and crushed the wooden gate to pieces. She galloped towards the prince with tears of happiness falling from her eyes. The guards at the gate thought she was trying to attack the prince and before the prince had time to shout his order, they had already cut down the poor buffalo mother with their swords.

The prince knelt down to hold the head of the dying buffalo mother. He cried desperately and regretted having forgotten the unselfish love of the buffalo mother, even for a moment. From that day on the buffalo mother´s spirit named Bago Medaw *nat* has been guarding the well-being of the people of Pegu. You may see an image of a beautiful woman wearing a buffalo helmet standing inside a small wooden temple built in her honour, still today.

AUNGZWAMAGYI
Lord of the White Horse

Captain Aungzwa was the bravest soldier in Prince Narapatisithu's army. The prince's half-brother King Naratheinhka of Pagan was a cruel and ruthless ruler, whom everybody was afraid of. Even though he built fine temples to add to the glory of magnificent Pagan, nobody really respected him because of his evil nature. Prince Narapatisithu had a beautiful wife. She was a jewel among the ladies at the royal court. When she walked in the palace gardens butterflies followed her, mistaking her for a sweet-smelling flower. The prince loved his wife dearly, not even taking any concubines, as was the custom of Burmese royalty in those days.

Unfortunately, King Naratheinhka also fell in love with the beautiful princess. To satisfy his burning desire, he invented a wicked plan. The king announced that a rebel group was terrorising the villages at the border. He ordered his brother Prince Narapatisithu to take his army, conquer the rebels and calm the villages. The king pretended that he could trust this mission only to his brother. At the same time he planned to persuade his wife to become one of his queens by lying to her, that her husband had died in the battle.

The prince had his doubts, but of course he had to obey the king's orders. He took his faithful Captain Aungzwa and his army and rode towards the border. When the troops reached the villages that were supposed to be in danger, and found the villagers working peacefully in their fields, the prince guessed that his beloved wife was in danger. He sent his trusted soldier Captain Aungzwa to kill the treacherous king. He gave the captain his best white horse so that he could reach the Royal City before the king's foul play would succeed. "If you kill this wicked king, who does not deserve to rule our great kingdom, you can choose one of his queens to be your wife".

Captain Aungzwa rose on the fine white horse and galloped away as fast as he could. He was in Pagan before midnight, and entered the palace bedrooms without anybody trying to prevent him. The captain was well known for his honesty and bravery. Not even the king's bodyguards questioned his sudden appearance in the royal quarters. Captain Aungzwa went into the king's chambers and cut the wicked king's head off. Next morning Prince Narapatisithu rode through the gates of Pagan triumphantly as the new king.

When the new king received the humble ministers, queens and concubines of the previous king, he announced that Captain Aungzwa was to be rewarded for his services by marrying one the queens. The proud queens were horrified. They knelt down in front of the king and begged to be saved from the humiliation of becoming wife to an ordinary soldier, no matter how brave. The king had a soft heart and listened to the queen's pleas. So he turned to the princesses. The princesses were also disgusted at the thought of marrying a soldier. "Please kill us rather than force us marry a soldier!" they cried. The king could not resist and he gave in to the womens' tears.

Captain Aungzwa was summoned in front of the Golden Throne. King Narapatisithu was sitting there in all his glory. His faithful wife was there beside him. All the queens and princesses sat round the throne, looking down at Captain Aungzwa, who was undeniably handsome in his red uniform. Some of the princesses secretly sighed, but turned their noses further up in the air anyhow.

"For your services to the king and the kingdom, my faithful Aungzwa, I promised to reward you with a wife of your choice. Please choose from these beautiful daughters of my ministers," said King Narapatisithu, nodding towards the far corner of the hall. There sat the maidens with downcast eyes, hoping to be chosen by the handsome captain. But Aungzwa was surprised and disappointed! Was he not the bravest and the most trustworthy of all king's officers? Did he not risk his own life by entering the king's bedrooms with a sword in his hand? Was he not good enough for these fancy ladies? Before he could watch his words, an angry "PTSHIH!" slipped from his mouth. The king could not tolerate this kind of behaviour in front of the whole court. Disrespect had to be punished and there was only one way: death.

After Captain Aungzwa had died, he became a *nat* spirit. He used to ride on a white horse in the king's nightmares. King Narapatisithu regretted his hasty decision. He should not have changed his mind about the reward only because of womens' tears, for they are endless when it comes to getting their way. King Narapatisithu declared Captain Aungzwa to be respected as a Royal *Nat Myinbyushin*, the Lord of the White Horse.

When the Burmese troops were fighting against the invading British during the First Anglo-Burmese War in 1824-1826, many soldiers swore they saw a man dressed in ancient red uniform riding a white horse towards the enemy lines, behind the famous General Mahabandoola holding a shining sword high up above his head. And again, when the Shwenandaw in Mandalay, the Golden Palace of the last kings of Burma was bombed by British troops and burned in Mandalay in the last days of the Second World War, the very same soldier was seen fighting the flames together with the Burmese.

Captain Aungzwa was faithful to the kings and Kingdom of Burma to the end. Today you may see a wooden white horse in the bazaar. If you buy it and donate it as a present to the faithful captain, he will take care of your safety too.

LADY THON BAN HLA

Long ago, when King Duttabaung ruled his mighty kingdom, there lived a beautiful maiden called Thon Ban Hla, "Three Times Beautiful". She was called that because she was beautiful in the morning, beautiful at noon and beautiful in the evening too. The kings of Burma have always had a weakness for female beauty, and when Duttabaung heard a rumour of this exceptional maiden, he decided to make her one of his queens.

Thon Ban Hla lived very far from the Royal City and so King Duttabaung sent his trusted general to make the marriage arrangements with the girl's parents and to escort the bride safely to the palace. The general of course obeyed the king's order.

When he arrived at Thon Ban Hla's village and saw the beautiful maiden he could not help himself, but fell in love with her. On the way to the Royal City, Thon Ban Hla, who was not accustomed to the smooth courtesies of the court, also fell head over hells in love with the handsome general in his purple uniform. As the Royal City came closer, the two lovers became more desperate. How could they prevent the king from marrying her and still save their lives?

On the last day of the journey, the general came up with a plan. He left Thon Ban Hla outside the Royal City walls, in a small cosy cottage, and went bravely to face his king. Bowing his head to the ground he said: "My Lord, I have obeyed your order and found the maiden called Thon Ban Hla, from the village. I brought her here, but I have to tell you the rumour of her beauty was only partly true. Her face is very beautiful, but she is so fat, that I had to leave her outside the city gates, as she could not get through them." The king was horrified by this surprising piece of news. He at once lost all interest in Thon Ban Hla, and just felt lucky that his general had thought of his honour and not embarrassed him by bringing such a bride to the palace.

Thon Ban Hla and the cunning general lived happily together in the small cottage outside the Royal City walls for a time. Then the general began to miss his hunting trips with other officers and the lively atmosphere of the court. In the beginning he stayed away for only a few hours, but then he could be away for weeks. Thon Ban Hla was sad and lonely. Further, she noticed that there was a baby on the way.

One day, the handsome general did not come back any more. Thon Ban Hla lived alone in her cottage making her modest livelihood by weaving beautiful cloths, which she sold to the court ladies. In due time she gave birth to a chubby-cheeked little baby girl, whom she called Nemi. But even the happiness of getting a daughter did not take away the aching of her broken heart.

After few years of suffering, Thon Ban Hla died. Soon after that her little daughter also died. They both became *nats*, like so many who die before their time from heartache or trough injustice.

The little girl Shin Nemi became the special guardian *nat* of children. Even today, every year before the final exams in school, the Burmese children donate toys and duck eggs to Shin Nemi *nat* in return for good success at school. When a baby smiles in her sleep, the Burmese parents say that Shin Nemi is playing the flute.

Tales

THE HARP MASTER

Once upon a time there was a famous harp master living in the village of Dagon, where the magnificent Shwedagon pagoda stands shining like a golden mountain. When the harp master played his instrument, even the *nats* stopped and listened. Many young men came from all over Burma to study this music and the gentle hearted master always agreed to teach each one of them. One of his students was San Oo Maung. The young man was exceptionally talented and the harp master hoped he would continue the age-old tradition of the great masters of Burmese harp music. When San Oo Maung played, everyone thought it was the master himself. Being praised like this, San Oo Maung began to think secretly that he was already better than his teacher was. Young men are often inpatient and eager to become famous, so San Oo Maung challenged his old master in a harp-playing contest.

The challenge came as a shock to the old master. He did not wish to compete, since he thought the art of music is not a weapon in a battle but a tool to smooth the restless mind by hearing the quiet sounds of peace. But people were eager to see who would play the harp better. Even the King of Ava was on his way to the village curious to see such an interesting competition.

The old master was worried. He tossed and turned sleeplessly in his bed thinking how to solve the matter of the competition without hurting his student and also without losing face himself. Thagya Min, the King of Deva Nats was a great fan of harp music. The old master was his particular favourite because of his modesty and kind heart. Now, the King of Deva Nats sits on his golden throne in heaven. When someone on earth has a problem, his celestial seat turns hard and uncomfortable. In that way Thagya Min knows when to check on the human world and who needs his help. Seeing the old harp master troubled, Thagya Min took the form of a wandering hermit (as he often does) and descended to Dagon village. He went to the harp master's house in the morning. When the old master's wife offered him breakfast, he got the chance to talk with the master himself. The master poured his heart out to the wise hermit, Thagya Min in disguise.

"Don't worry, venerable master!" said the hermit, "I will advise you how to teach a lesson to that ambitious young rival of yours without hurting him or your honour." Then he told the master to begin the competition with his best song. After that, with every song that followed he should cut off one string of his harp until the young competitor gave up. The old harp master was very surprised on hearing such strange advice. He looked carefully into the eyes of the smiling hermit and on seeing a golden glimmer in them, he promised to do as he requested.

When the day of the competition finally came, there were thousands of people everywhere. The King of Ava was sitting with his favourite little prince on the highest seat. Under his feet were all the fine ladies of the court, the ministers in their purple gowns and soldiers and bodyguards in their shining armour. The ordinary people had been flocking to the village since the day before. There were food stalls, palmists and souvenir shops everywhere. The atmosphere was excited and happy. In heaven, Thagya Min and his *deva nats* had also taken their seats. The old master and San Oo Maung climbed on the bamboo stage, which was built in the middle of the village, so that everyone could see and hear what was going on. First the old master played his most beautiful song. It was so lovely, that many people cried. But San Oo Maung was not less skilful. He had been taught by the best, and so his music travelled over the amazed audience like moonlight on still waters. After both competitors had finished their first song, everyone was even more excited. What would come out of this! Which one would win?

When the time came for the master to play the next song, he took out his dagger and cut off one silk string from his harp. And he played as beautifully as before. San Oo Maung was surprised at his master's action, but followed bravely this new turn of the competition. After thirteen songs, when there was but one silken string left in each of their harps, he gave up. He acknowledged his defeat and bowing down in front of his old teacher gave great merit to him as the true master of the art of the Burmese harp. People applauded approvingly.

But the old master lifted his dagger one more time and cut off the last string. The audience became absolutely silent. You could have heard even the wind tiptoeing, but the wind also stood still, waiting breathlessly. The old master held his black and red harp gently in his lap and played one more song. The sound was as if heavenly bells had turned into diamonds. A sweet smell of jasmine and rose surrounded the master, San Oo Maung, the King of Ava and all the audience. The music seemed to reach up to the sky from where the *deva nats* accompanied the melody with their celestial instruments. People realised that Thagya Min had helped the old master in order to give a lesson to his ungrateful student. San Oo Maung understood that he owed all his talent and skill to his patient teacher who had taught him everything. San Oo Maung was ashamed of challenging his kind teacher and he begged for his forgiveness. That the old master gave without a moments hesitation.

After that day San Oo Maung was by the masters side, serving him as he would serve his own father.

THE WISE GIRL

Long ago in the royal city of Ava there lived a beautiful and wise girl called Ma Sabe, with her old blind mother. She had a gentle heart and many people came to ask for her advice and help when they had problems. She earned her living by weaving lovely *longyis* for the ladies of the king's court. The King of Ava was very fond of young and beautiful wives. Even though he already had three hundred of them, he still wished to have new ones.

One morning Ma Sabe was entering the Golden Palace gates carrying her *longyis* in a basket over her head. The king happened to ride out mounted on his white elephant. The king's greedy eye spotted the graceful body and delicate little face of Ma Sabe, even though she tried to stay in the shadow of the big trees with her eyes modestly downcast. At once the king ordered the *mahout* to stop the elephant and sent his special minister to enquire whom this incomparable beauty was. On that very same day the minister appeared at Ma Sabe's house requesting her mother's permission for the royal marriage. Ma Sabe listened behind a curtain with a trembling heart. She certainly did not wish to become one of the king's unhappy wives, living in their golden prison behind the palace walls. Further, there was a certain young and handsome blacksmith in the village, who had won Ma Sabe's love. To the minister's annoyed surprise and to Ma Sabe's great relief her blind mother refused to give her daughter's hand. Now the kings of Burma were absolute monarchs, who ruled over the life and death of their subjects, but even they could not force parents to give their daughters in marriage if they did not wish to do so. In Burma the parents are the king and queen of their children. But so great was the king's desire that he made a wicked plan to win Ma Sabe as his wife.

Next day the King of Ava rode out from the palace dressed in his most valuable golden armour. He wore a high jewelled helmet and had huge rubies in his ears. When he and his troops arrived at Ma Sabe's house all the people of the city rushed to see what was going to happen. The king lifted a red velvet bag in his hand for everyone to see: "I have here two stones, one black and one white. Ma Sabe is to choose one of them right in front of you all. If she chooses the white stone, I will leave her in peace to continue her everyday life as a weaver. But if she chooses the black stone, she must follow me here and now to become my queen in the Royal Palace." People mumbled that this seemed to be a fair deal for the girl since it would be her *kan* that decided which stone she would take. Ma Sabe was not so sure if *kan* would have any part in this particular game. She strongly suspected the king of a foul play. And she was quite right. The king had secretly put two black stones inside the red velvet bag.

But beautiful Ma Sabe was not praised for being quick-witted and wise for nothing. She bravely put her hand inside the bag, took a stone and peaked at it keeping it closed tightly in her little fist. Then she started to sing and dance happily at the same time throwing the stone far behind the surprised soldiers and on-lookers in the river behind her house. Ma Sabe bowed deep in front of the astonished king and said: "Forgive me Your Majesty! I was so happy that I don't have to leave my old mother alone that I did not know what I was doing! I threw the stone to the river, but there is the other stone inside the bag and let us see what colour is that. If it is black then it must be the white stone that I threw to the river in my whim, isn´t it?" The king had been caught in his own trap and in front of so many witnesses he could only turn his mount around and ride pack to the palace embarrassed.

Never again did the king try to lure young girls to his palace, but grew old and grey with the three hundred wives he already had. Ma Sabe married her handsome blacksmith and lived happily with him and their children ever after.

RICH BOY DOES NOT LEARN

In the gem city of Mogok there lived a very rich couple. They owned a huge ruby mine and were also dealing in jade and gold. They were so wealthy that they did not know what to do with their money, because the one thing they wanted most could not be bought with money. And that was a son. They tried to live a good life practising charity and kindness to all living beings. Finally, after many years of hope and prayer, the wife became pregnant. In due time a chubby little boy was born. His face was round like a full moon and his hair black like the wing of a crow. You can imagine that the rich couple could not be happier even if Thagya Min himself was a guest in their home.

The parents named the son Maung Pyin Nyar and they loved him so much that they let him do whatever he wished. Maung Pyin Nyar had his personal servants to feed him his favourite foods and to play with him. The little rascal soon became spoilt, since the servants did not dare to scold him even when he was naughty and pinched them. When it was time for him to go to school, he cried and begged his mother not to make him study. The poor mother's heart was soft, and she could not force her only son to what he did not want to do.

So Maung Pyin Nyar grew up without knowing how to read or write. His parents were so rich they thought their son and even his son would be safe. Maung Pyin Nyar had a lot of friends and he gambled and had parties with them every night. In the daytime he slept, and ate the delicacies his servants brought to him. He became fat and lazy. His black hair was thinning even before he turned 25 years of age, because of the strenuous nightlife.

And then quite suddenly, his loving parents passed away. At first Maung Pyin Nyar did not know what to do. He turned to his friends for help and let the servants run the household. He did not understand that the people whom he considered his friends were just greedy and selfish. They lied to him and got him involved in fake businesses. The servants, who he had been teasing and pinching since childhood thought it was now time to get even. Everyone cheated him, but Maung Pyin Nyar had enough money to spend. It is harder to make an honest *kyat* than spend a thousand of somebody else's money! Maung Pyin Nyar had never worked a day in his life, and his so-called friends were all very skilled swindlers. This was the opportunity they had been waiting for years, pretending to be his best friends. Soon all the money was gone.

Maung Pyin Myar sold the ruby mines, the jade and gold shops and even the house were he was born. To his surprise also his friends were gone by the time his last *kyats* were spent. He went to their houses to have a little food or borrow some money, but they did not even bother to come out to meet him. Now he really got worried. What could he do for work, since he did not know how to read and write? Maung Pyin Nyar had no other choice except to beg for his food on the sidewalks. People did not have any pity on him, because they had seen how he spent his parents' money on drinking parties and gambling. Even his old servants did not drop a *pya* in his begging bowl. Maung Pyin Nyar was hungry, miserable and lonely.

At the same time Maung Pyin Nyar's parents were watching the sad state of their only son from the celestial palace gardens of Thagya Min. They felt so much pity on their son that they begged the King of the *Deva Nats* for a chance to help him. The kind hearted Thagya Min gave them permission, but emphasised that they could help him only once. The happy parents sent a *deva nat* in the disguise of an old woman to meet their son.

Next morning the dirty and now very slim Maung Pyin Nyar was begging for his food at the corner of the fruit market. The *deva nat* dressed as an old woman came along the road carrying an ordinary looking clay pot. When he asked for money, she put the pot into his hands saying: "This pot is the last thing left of your parents legacy. Use it wisely." Then the old woman disappeared. Maung Pyin Nyar was surprised. He looked in the pot and when he found it empty he said: "Silly old hag! Instead of giving me this ugly old pot, she could have put a few *kyats* in it!" As he uttered these words, the pot became full of money. Maung Pyin Nyar realised it was a magical pot sent by his parents. But the ungrateful son did not even bother to go to a pagoda to thank his parents. No, he rushed in to the nearest restaurant and ordered all kinds of foods.

Soon his old friends heard about his change of luck. Even the old servants came back to seek employment. Maung Pyin Nyar bought a house and continued his carefree life with his untrustworthy friends. He spent more money than ever before. Life was easy thanks to the magic pot, which was always full of money.

One night Maung Pyin Nyar had ordered a *zat pwé* theatre group to play and dance for him. He drank rum and watched the dance of an actor playing the part of *zawgyi* the magician. The *zawgyi* dancer was throwing a silver pot high up in the air and catching it skilfully again. Drunken Maung Pyin Nyar wanted to entertain his friends by imitating the dancer. He took his magic pot in his hands and also began to throw it high up. But Maung Pyin Nyar was neither a zawgyi nor a dancer. He was just a clumsy drunkard. The magical pot crushed down at his feet, and before the morning dawned his money and friends were gone.

For days he waited for the old woman to appear again in the fruit market. For weeks he begged his food on the roadside. People who had seen him making the same mistake twice did not have any pity on him. They told him to leave the city and live in the jungle. His mother and father cried in the celestial palace gardens when they saw their son walking out of the city gates. For a time Maung Pyin Nyar lived in a simple hut in the jungle, but then he disappeared. No one ever saw him again.

Burmese parents tell this story to their children who are too lazy to go to school or don't feel like helping with the household work.

GOLDEN BOY

There lived a happy couple in the gentle green shade of the bamboos, just outside the royal city of Amarapura. In due time they had a baby son, whose skin was shining like gold. They named him Ko Shwe, the Golden Boy. The family lived a peaceful life, tending their fields and collecting fruits and vegetables from the garden. Ko Shwe grew strong and handsome. He was kind and unselfish, caring for his parents and helping anyone whom asked for his help.

Years went on, as they do, fast as a *hintha's* flight. The hair of Ko Shwe's parents turned white and they became blind. Ko Shwe took charge of all the household work. Early in the morning he went to the fields and when the sun was setting he returned carrying fresh fruit and water from the spring. One day two merchants were travelling through the forest towards the royal city when they saw a shining golden shape in the midst of the bamboos. As the sun was setting, the dim pink light tricked their eyes to mistake Ko Shwe for a golden deer. The two merchants were sure they saw a magical animal. The King of Amarapura, who was known to be very fond of hunting, might pay a handsome reward for this information!

The merchants went quickly to the Golden Palace to tell what they had seen in the forest. The king was of course excited. The very next day he would ride out for a hunting expedition. Next dawn the king's party left the royal city. They set up their camp in the bamboo bush not far from the old couple´s house. The day was bright and hot. The king sat patiently on his soft red velvet pillow, waiting in vain for the golden deer to appear.

Finally the sun turned ruby-red and the evening clouds blushed golden and pink. It was time for Ko Shwe to return to his parents. He decided to pick some mangoes for the evening meal as he walked through the green foliage, singing a happy song.

The king and his guards saw his golden shape moving behind the trees thinking it was a magical golden deer of the old legends. Oh, how he shone, like pure gold reflecting the last rays of the setting sun! The king lifted his bow and shot an arrow straight through Ko Shwe´s heart. The guards ran to collect what they thought was a golden deer, but to their surprise and horror, they found a dead boy lying on the ground whose skin shone like gold. The king also felt sad. He looked for the parents of the boy and carried his dead body to them himself. The mother and father cried desperately. Nothing in this world could comfort them!

Now Thagya Min rules in the Tavatimsa heaven of the *deva nats*. There he sits on a golden throne with many comfortable and soft pillows on it. When someone in the human abode is in trouble, these pillows turn hard as stone. That is how Thagya Min knows that it is time to check down on earth what is the problem is. Thagya Min keeps a book on the good and bad deeds of human beings, so he knew that the good-hearted Ko Shwe had died well before his time, and that his old blind parents were now in a desperate situation. Thagya Min took the form of a wandering hermit and went to the old couple´s house.

After listening to the sad story of losing their beloved son, the King of Deva Nats in hermit´s disguise spoke: "Please do not cry.

You know that human life and happiness are but temporary. Nothing is permanent except change. But since you are good people, practising all the virtues in this life, I will grant you one wish. Tell me, do you want to be rich or do you wish to have your eyesight back?" The old couple became silent for a while. The old man had guessed it was Thagya Min, the King of Deva Nats himself addressing them for no one else could grant such gifts. He bowed his head to the ground and said: "Venerable Sir, more than anything I would like to see my son returning home with a pot of gold on his head." This was a clever answer and soon they heard a familiar song from the path outside the house. The old couple looked around as now they could see, and ran to the door to meet their beloved son. When they turned back to thank the hermit, he had already vanished.

BEAUTIFUL BEYDAYI AND THE PRINCE

This story is two thousand years old and it tells how life is full of surprises and how *kan*, our destiny, leads the way.

The King of Burma had many queens and concubines. So many, that he lost all track of their number and forgot to show love to most of them. So it happened from time to time, that some minor queen fell in love with a handsome officer in the king's army. This, of course, was forbidden, and if the two lovers were ever found out, they had to suffer a severe punishment without mercy.

At the time of this story, a queen had a secret lover and she became pregnant. Fearing the king's anger, she hid her growing belly and in due time delivered a baby girl in the bamboo forest just outside the Royal Palace. She had to leave her newborn baby there, praying to the forest *nats* to keep her safe.

The baby soon became hungry and cried for milk. A hermit happened to walk by on his way to the hilltop pagoda. He heard her cry. When the hermit found the baby girl in the woods, he felt so much love and compassion towards her, that milk began to flow from his fingers. He fed her and took her to his grotto, which was both his hermitage and home.

The years went past quickly and the girl, whom the hermit had named Beydayi, grew up to be a beautiful maiden. Even though he had raised Beydayi as his own child, the hermit felt it not proper to have a young maiden around him all day. So he devised a plan to keep Beydayi away and busy the whole time. The hermit gave the girl a huge gourd shell with a tiny hole at the top and told her to go to the river to fetch water. The plan worked. Every morning Beydayi went down to the riverside, dipped the gourd shell in the water and waited for it to fill. It was late in the evening when she finally returned back to the hermitage.

At the same time, when Beydayi's mother was falling in love with her handsome officer, another love story took place in the neighbouring kingdom. There was a princess, who would not agree to marry any of the eligible suitors that asked for her hand. The old king had a soft heart and he promised to his youngest daughter that she could choose whomever she pleased.

Time went by, but the princess did not show any interest in the princes or sons of the ministers. Nobody knew that in the darkness of the night she had already given her heart to a lover. Every night a *naga* prince would come to her and take a human form. When the first rays of the sun appeared, he returned to his underground kingdom in his snake form.

One young and ambitious prince was very eager to marry the princess and to inherit the kingdom after her father. He decided to sneak to her chamber and charm her with his romance. He hid himself behind a curtain and waited for the servants to leave. When the princess lay down on her bed, he was about to come out from his hiding place. But a strange hissing sound stopped him: to his horror he saw a huge king cobra appearing through an open window and moving towards the royal bed. The prince jumped out from the curtains with a sword in his hands and chopped the princess's lover to pieces before she could stop him. The princess was desperate to see her dead lover, but the king congratulated the prince for saving the his daughter's life. He at once arranged a wedding.

What no one knew, was that she was already pregnant with the *naga* prince's child. In due time she gave birth to twin brothers. Like many snakes, also these two sons of the *naga* were blind. Now the princess's secret had been revealed. The two young princes were unwelcome reminders of the princess's love affair and considered unworthy to be heirs of the throne. The princess begged her father the king to save the lives of the innocent children. So they were put on a raft and sent floating down the river.

The two brothers travelled a long way. They learned to find fruit and catch fish and they grew to become strong and handsome. One day the raft happened to get caught in the branches of a flowering tree, where a beautiful female *nat* lived. She fell in love with the younger prince and promised to cure their eyes if he agreed to stay and marry her. (The tree *nats* can only wander away from their home as far as its shadow reaches.) The prince of course promised to do this. Soon she mixed some herbs and started the treatment. Little by little the twin princes regained their eyesight.

Years went by and the young princes began to feel restless, as young men always do. The younger brother made a solemn promise to return one day to his faithful tree *nat* and so they continued their river journey. One afternoon their raft floated past the place where beautiful Beydayi was collecting water. The elder prince saw her sweet and serious face concentrating on her work, and at once lost his heart to her. He guided the raft to the shore and asked the girl what she was doing with such a huge gourd shell. Beydayi replied with shy downcast eyes that she was carrying water to her father up in the hill hermitage. The princes could hardly hide their laughter on see-ing that she was earnest. The elder prince took his sword and cut the gourd shell open: "Let me help and take the water to your father" he said. Beydayi agreed and up the hill they went.

The princes presented themselves before the hermit, who saw they were sons of a royal house. The elder prince asked the hermit for Beydayi's hand and they were duly married the same evening. They had a son, who was destined to become the powerful King Duttabaung, the builder of the Royal City of Srikshettra.

This old story reminds us, that even if good luck has deserted us, events can turn in our favour, if that is our destiny.

THREE SONS –THREE KYATS

An old farmer had worked hard in the rice fields all his life. He had a pretty little house, a buffalo and two papaya trees casting a cool shadow over the yard. He also had three strong sons, all of whom he could be proud of.

One afternoon, after ploughing the fields, the old farmer felt very very tired. He sat in his chair and wondered, what would become of his household when he was gone. "All my sons are good workers, and they have done their best to help me. Since their mother passed away, I have tried to bring them up alone. They should soon find wives and start their family life. This farm and the fields are too small to divide into three. But how can I find out, who would be worthy to continue my lifelong work here?" The old farmer sat there in deep thoughts until the sun set behind the distant hills, casting the pink and golden light of a Burmese evening.

After supper, the old farmer summoned his sons. He said: "I am already getting old and weary. It is time for me to step down and let one of you continue my work. The two others will have to leave and find happiness somewhere else." The three sons were worried about their father's health, but the old farmer raised his hand, reassuring them that he was fine. "I am not going anywhere yet, my beloved sons. Here, I give each of you one *kyat* note. I want you to go and buy anything, that would fill up the storage room." The sons were surprised to hear their father's words, but of course they obeyed him without question.

In the morning all three brothers went out early. The oldest son walked outside the village. There was a field of tall grass growing. For the whole hot day he cut the grass. In the afternoon he carried it to his home and filled the storage room with it. When the tough day's job was done and ready, he went to the teahouse and treated himself to a well deserved pot of tea with the *kyat* his father had given him.

The middle son went down to the riverside. For the whole hot day he dug buckets full of soft silver sand. In the afternoon he carried it to his home and filled the storage room with it. When the tough job was done and ready, he went to the teahouse and treated himself to a well deserved pot of tea with the *kyat* his father had given him.

The youngest son went to the family rice fields, as he had done every morning of his life. For the whole hot day he worked hard tilling the land. In the cool of the evening, when women prepare for the supper and men sit in the teahouses chatting about this and that, the youngest son went to the village shop. He bought a candle and matches with the *kyat* his father had given him.

After the meal, the old farmer asked how his three sons had spent the money he had given them. The oldest and the middle son showed their storage rooms full of fresh cut grass and silver sand. The old farmer nodded his head but did not say anything. When it was the youngest brother's turn to open his storage room, he took the candle and matches out of his pocket. The older and the middle brother laughed heartily about such foolishness. But the youngest brother went into the dark storage room, lit the candle and – there, soft flickering light filled the room up!

The old farmer smiled and hugged his youngest son. "To you I will leave this house, rice fields and everything else. Your older brothers filled the rooms alright, but they used the money for their own refreshment. You have invested the money cleverly and still worked the whole day on the fields."

The two older brothers soon left their old home, got married and lived happily with their families in the next village. The youngest son also married, had three sons and took care of his old father until he quietly passed away. This story teaches how it is not necessarily the quantity of things that matter, but the quality, and how important it is to put things in the right order.

FARMER AND ROBBERS

Near the ancient city of Pegu there was a small village. Every family in the village made their living in the vast rice fields spreading towards every point of the compass and as far as one's eye could see. Sometimes during the busy season young and strong boys from the village went and helped in other people's fields in order to earn some extra money for their families. You can imagine that working in the rice field is very hard: the midday sun is merciless and in the evening you feel as if your back was beaten by the most fearful *Balu* King with his heavy club.

Ko Nyunt had been working for a whole week in the hot fields and now he was returning home with five *kyats* tied in the knot of his *pasoe*. Five *kyats* is not very much, not even one dollar, but for a poor family like Ko Nyunt's, it was a lot. In the evening they would eat fish. His little sisters and brothers would have steamed peanuts that they liked so much. For his mother he planned to buy sweet smelling jasmine for her hair and for father – a big green *cheerot* cigar!

Ko Nyunt walked along the road forgetting his aching back and his sun-burned neck. He smiled as he went along, imagining the loving smiles of his family when they saw him coming. At the same time ten pairs of dark eyes were watching his happy stroll from behind the bushes.

Suddenly Ko Nyunt's journey was disrupted by ten scary looking and heavily tattooed tall men. The robbers surrounded him shouting terrible threats. The biggest and hairiest robber stepped forward. "Give us your money and valuables peacefully and we will let you go!" he said with a low voice that reminded Ko Nyunt of a tiger growling. "Mr. Robber, if you look at me carefully, you can see I am a poor boy from the village. Why do you want to rob me?" replied Ko Nyunt without fear, and with no intention of giving up his hard work's earnings. The robber came closer, and pushed Ko Nyunt to the ground. Ko Nyunt climbed back just to get an angry blow on his nose from the robber's fist. But Ko Nyunt was no coward! He fought back with all his powers, thinking all the time of his family back home.

Finally the robber had to call his companions to help. The ten robbers together tied fierce Ko Nyunt back and searched his clothes. Of course they found the five *kyats* tied in the knot of his *pasoe*, for that is the place Burmese men keep their money safe. "What in the name of forest *nats*! Did you fight for these five miserable *kyats*? Do you not understand that we could have killed you?" shouted the astonished leader of the robbers. "Let that crazy boy get to his feet!" Ko Nyunt struggled up, snatched his precious five *kyats* from the hands of the robber and said calmly: "I worked hard for this money. It is therefore more valuable to me that all the stolen riches in the kingdom."

The leader of the robbers stepped back and bowed to him respectfully. Then and there he made a solemn vow not to rob and steal any more in his life, but to change and work honestly. And this promise he kept until the end of his days.

FATHER'S LOVE NEVER DIES

Long ago, in the kingdom of Ava, there lived a wise and good hearted king. He built many famous pagodas and also took care of his peoples' everyday life. Irrigation canals were dug at the king's expense and he donated money to the poor people. The kingdom lived in peace with its neighbours and everyone was happy and contented. Everyone, except the king and his queen. They had hoped for a son or a daughter, but were never blessed with children of their own.

One day a wandering *yathein* came to the Royal City. He was a very famous fortune-teller, and the queen was curious to hear what the future would bring, as women always are. She summoned the famous *yathein* to her reception hall. The *yathein* came, bowed to the ground, asked her date of birth and other important questions. After that he bent down to make all sorts of calculations on a little blackboard he carried with him, mumbling strange words to himself.

"Milady, you will experience the greatest joy and the darkest despair a woman can feel: you will have a son, whose destiny it is to kill his own father and to die in misery. This is the *kan* of your family, and no good deeds in this life can change it," prophecied the *yathein*. The Queen was very alarmed, but she tried to calm herself thinking: "My beloved husband has wished a child from me for years. I am already getting old. Maybe the *yathein* calculated wrong."

After a few weeks the queen felt very sick in the morning. She called the palace doctors and they announced her that she was expecting a child. The Queen was horrified. The first part of the *yathein's* prophesy had come true. The doctors ran to inform the king's ministers and the ministers brought the happy message to the king. The king was naturally overjoyed! He arranged a huge *pwé* for all the people in his kingdom. The party lasted for three days and everyone congratulated the king on his good fortune.

Only the queen was silent. Secretly she made arrangements to meet a widow, who lived outside the Royal City and who was known to practise magic. But nothing stays secret in court and the king's favourite minister heard about these arrangements. The king was surprised. He at once ordered the queen in front of him and questioned as to what in heaven's name she was up to. Crying desperately the queen fell down at his feet and told him about the prophecy. "Lord of my life, I cannot bear to think that I would be carrying your murderer inside me. Please let me get rid of this unfortunate child!" The King lifted his wife gently from the ground and said: "Wipe your eyes darling. We are very lucky to have a son. I will love him dearly, and nothing bad will happen."

Time went by, and the royal couple celebrated the birth of their son, together with everybody in the kingdom. The little prince was often sick and his father the king stayed by his bed day and night. Nobody could have loved his son more. One time the little prince hurt his finger while practising with bow and arrow. The wound was infected and a painful boil grew on the finger. The little prince cried. He could not sleep because of the pain. The king came to take care of him as usual. He tucked his son in under the cool silken sheets and put his aching finger with the boil in it into his mouth. The warmth helped, and soon the little prince slept peacefully. During the night the boil became ripe and burst, but the king did not have the heart to wake his son. So he just quietly swallowed the substance from the boil.

After many more years, the prince grew up and despite his father's tender love, turned out to be exceptionally cruel and short-tempered. Everyone from the ministers and generals down to the palace cooks and gardeners were afraid of him. He spent his time in bad company, who planned to benefit from him when the time came. They whispered ugly words in his ears about how grand a king he would be.

One day, after the prince had been beating the king's favourite minister for no reason, the king wanted to talk about his ruthless behaviour. The king did not have a chance to say a word before his son threatened his life with a long sword. The prince ordered his wicked friends to capture the king and throw him into the darkest jail. The king was not to have any food or drink, and anybody trying to smuggle him anything even as small as a pea would at once lose his head.

The queen trembled with horror and shed tears of helplessness. She tried to think of a way to help her husband before he starved to death. After a few days, when the king was already quite weak, she covered her arms with a thick layer of butter, and covered in a silken scarf walked bravely past the guards into her husband's prison. Once there, she nearly fainted when she saw her beloved husband so weak and dirty. "You should have listened to the *yathein's* prophecy. Look now how we suffer because of that creature who calls himself your son!" the queen cried. "Hush my lovely wife. He is my son, and nothing can make me love him less. I will forgive him his foolishness and pray that Thagya Min in the heavens would do the same." Then he licked a little butter from his wife's arms. Next morning he was found dead.

When the message of the king's passing reached the queen, she lost any wish to continue her life. She put on her official court dress, which shone with gold and jewels like the costumes of the *deva nats*. She marched to the king's reception hall, where her son was giving orders to his troops. Without fear she walked up to him and said: "How dare you call yourself the king! Your father the king is dead, and you are not fit to sit on his throne." Then she told him about the *yathein's* prophecy a long time ago, and how his father tended his hurting finger, and what his last words were so full of forgiveness and love for this wicked son.

Finally the prince's eyes opened. He understood how much his father had loved him and how all the power and riches of this world could not even replace the smallest part of what he had lost today, when his father died. The prince became mad with guilt and despair. He rushed out from the palace and the Royal City. A few days after he was seen wandering the streets of Ava looking for his father and begging forgiveness from everyone he met.

GOSSIPMONGER GETS HIS JUST DESERT

Ko Than was a hunter in a small village. Every morning he went out to the forests to check his traps. All the households in the village bought their meat from Ko Than, so he did reasonably well.

One day Ko Than wandered a little further into the forest than usual. By the end of the afternoon he had got lost in the wilderness. He knew very well that night is the time for more powerful hunters than he is, namely the tigers, and he certainly did not wish to become the prey. Ko Than was desperate and very much afraid. He rushed through the bamboos and high grass and finally came to a small clearing.

In the middle of the clearing stood a simple hut. Ko Than ran to the doorway, but stopped there surprised. A *yathein* in his brown robes and tall hat came out, with a kind smile on his face. But what a nose he had! Ko Than had never seen such a long nose. A baby elephant might be jealous! Seeing his guest standing there with his mouth open, the *yathein* asked what the problem was and if he could help. Ko Than recovered a little, and remembered his original worry at being lost in the forest. But still he could not take his eyes off from the *yathein's* nose.

The *yathein* served his guest food and tea, as is the hospitable custom in Burma. Then he said: "Dear guest, I will of course show you a safe way back to your village, but you must promise not to tell anyone about my nose." This Ko Than promised, eager to get home quickly.

Next morning Ko Than's wife gave him breakfast and asked where he had been so late the previous evening. Ko Than explained how he had lost his way. Then he lowered his voice and said: "You would not believe what I saw there in the deep forest. If I tell you, you must promise that you do not tell anyone about it." Of course his wife promised, and Ko Than described vividly the *yathein*, whose nose would make a baby elephant jealous.

Later the day, Ko Than's wife went to wash laundry in the river. There she could not resist telling her friends about her husband's adventure. The *yathein's* nose grew a little longer and when the wives told the story to their husbands in the evening, the nose had became as long as the trunk of a female elephant. Next day the men of the village went to the bazaar in the Royal City. In a week, the news about a *yathein* with a nose as long as the trunk of Ayeyarwady, the elephant king and mighty mount of Thagya Min himself, had reached the ears of the king.

Now the king was a very curious man. He wanted to see such a nose with his own eyes. The king sent for the village hunter Ko Than and told him to go and bring this amazing *yathein* in front of the Royal Court. Ko Than could not but obey.

Embarrassed he kneeled down in front of the *yathein's* hut. He explained how the story about the nose had slipped from him and now the whole kingdom knew about it. The *yathein* was a wise man. He said: "I will accept the king's invitation to come to the Royal Court. But since my nose is so long, it is difficult for me to walk such a long way. I guess you have to carry me on your back." And so the *yathein* climbed on Ko Than's back and they began their journey through the forest.

Yathein's nose might resemble a baby elephant's nose, but he also weighted as much! Ko Than staggered along the way until they finally came to the Royal City. Everybody turned to look at a red-faced and sweating Ko Than carrying the *yathein* with a long nose on his back. Once in the Palace, Ko Than fell down exhausted.

The king came with his queens and concubines, princes and princesses and all the other members of the court. They wondered about the *yathein's* exceptional nose, but soon lost their interest. "You may carry him back to his home", said the king to Ko Than. There was nothing else for Ko Than to do, than carry the *yathein* back to his forest home. On his way he decided not to gossip any more for the rest of his life.

It is always easy to let words fly from your mouth, but many times the results are very heavy to carry!

Fables

UNGRATEFUL SON

Once upon a time there lived an old couple in a simple bamboo hut by the mighty river Irrawaddy. One morning the old woman went to wash some laundry when she saw a huge tree trunk floating in the swift mid stream. Struggling on that trunk a tiger, a monkey, a snake and a young boy were holding on tight for their dear lives. The river Irrawaddy may look peaceful on the surface but the under-currents were strong and dangerous.

The old woman quickly ran to get her husband and together they pulled the trunk on shore. The tiger, the monkey and the snake bowed their heads at the feet of the old couple. "Thank you for saving our lives. From this day on we are your faithful servants," the grateful animals said in one voice. The boy introduced himself as Ko Maung, still shivering with fear and tiredness, also thanked the old couple. The old couple did not wish to hear any of this, but took them all under their roof, fed them and cared for them as if they were their children.

After a few days the tiger came to talk with the old couple. He said: " Thanks to your compassion and care I was rescued from death. My life belongs to you now. My strength has recovered and I will now return to my jungle home. If you ever need my help, just whisper my name to the jungle, and I will come at once." Then he bowed his majestic head and leaped into the jungle.

Next day the monkey bowed his hairy face in front of the old couple. He said: " Thanks to your compassion and care I was rescued from death. My life belongs to you now. My strength has recovered and I will now return to my jungle home. If you ever need my help, just whisper my name to the jungle, and I will come at once." Then he swung his long tail and disappeared in the foliage of jungle trees.

On the third day the snake coiled up in front of the old couple and said: " Thanks to your compassion and care I was rescued from death. My life belongs to you now. My strength has recovered and I will now return to my jungle home. If you ever need my help, just whisper my name to the jungle, and I will come at once." Then he waved his hooded head and vanished between the stones into the jungle. Only Ko Maung was left, and since the couple did not have any children of their own, they asked him to stay and live as their son. Ko Maung did not have any place to go, so he stayed, promising solemnly to take care of the old couple as long as they lived.

Days passed peacefully. The old couple took care of their little garden and Ko Maung helped with the work. On one very hot day, the prince from the golden city of Pagan happened to ride along the riverside with his party going towards the palace. They had been travelling a long time and everybody was exhausted. The prince decided to rest for the hot humid hours of the afternoon and ordered the party to stop not far from the old couple's home. The prince wished to swim and so indeed he did. He took off all his silken clothes and left them on a stone together with his golden armour. Among his clothes there was a special jewel belt, which was a present from his father the king of Pagan. While the prince swam in the cool river, a curious crow saw the shining belt glimmering in the sun. The crows are by nature curious and very fond of shining things. This one flew down and stole the jewel belt. On his way back towards his nest the crow met a hungry falcon. The falcon attacked and when the crow cried out desperately, he dropped the belt. It happened to fall in the old couple's garden. At the same time the prince and all his soldiers were looking for the belt. Of course they could not find it and they had to continue their ride back to the Royal Palace without it.

Early next morning the old woman was tending her garden, when she saw the jewelled belt shining in the middle of her herbs and vegetables. She took it inside, showed it to her husband and Ko Maung and said: "This must be a valuable belt. Someone very rich and powerful has lost it. We should keep it safe for his return, because surely he will be coming back this way to search such a beautiful thing." The old man packed the jewelled belt into a lacquerware box and hid if safely under the southeast pole of the house, under the protective eyes of the household guardian Min Mahagiri. Unfortunately Ko Maung had a different opinion on what should be done with the belt. He had a wicked idea of how to become rich without having to work for it. When the old couple returned to the garden, he quickly dug the box up, took the jewel belt and ran to the Royal City. Ko Maung planned to sell the jewels from the belt one by one, so that no one would suspect him of stealing the belt. But when he passed the gates to the city of Pagan he heard everyone talking about the great reward the king had promised to the person who would return the prince´s lost belt. Ko Maung realised that this could be a safer chance for him, since there were always many risks when a poor boy tried to sell huge rubies in the market. Somebody would certainly ask questions.

Ko Maung invented an evil plan. He ran back to the old couple´s hut, hid the jewel belt under the southeast pole of the house and went again to the Royal City. This time he sought to see the King of

Pagan in person. He claimed to know who stole the jewel belt. When he finally got to bow in front of the king and the prince, he accused the old couple of the theft. He explained where the belt was hidden and before the day was over, the old couple was thrown into the gaol of the palace. The old couple were terrified. They did not understand what had happened, and especially they were worried about their adopted son Ko Maung. Of course they did not know that the ungrateful son was behind their misery. The old woman cried and said: "My beloved husband. It is time to call for our faithful animal friends for help."

First came the tiger. He looked with sad eyes through the iron bars, but with all his strength he could not help the old couple. Next arrived the monkey. He reached his hand through the prison window, but could not do much except comfort the old couple. Last came the snake. Many people believe that the snakes are the wisest of all animals. The snake crawled in easily through the barred window and listened carefully to what the old couple told him. The snake spoke: "Don't worry my beloved parents. I know a way to help you. As you might know, the family of snakes knows all the medicinal plants and herbs in the world. I will send my brothers tiger and monkey to collect a rare flower from the top of the secret snake mountain in the Shan country. When tomorrow morning the king's favourite young daughter walks in the palace garden, I will bite her little toe with my poison fang. The king's best doctors cannot save her, but you can, by making tea from the flower my brothers will bring tonight. I am sure the king will pardon you and gratefully hear your story after the recovery of his daughter." The snake went back to his animal brothers the tiger and the monkey, who had waited outside for his orders. The monkey sat on the back of the mighty tiger and off they rode towards the secret mountain, where a magical flower grows. In the darkest hour of the night they returned, exhausted but with the magical flower, which the old man carefully secured in his pocket. The snake hid himself under a rose in the palace garden.

Next morning the king's favourite little princess walked to the palace garden, as the snake had predicted. The snake stuck his venom into the princess's little toe, and she fell down unconscious. All the maids and ladies of the court cried out loudly. The best doctors in the kingdom were summoned to the palace. The king was worried and promised anything to the man who could rescue his daughter. So loud was the noise from the palace, that the old couple sitting in the goal heard it. They asked the guards to send a message to the king telling him that they could save the little princess. The king at once ordered the old couple to be brought to the palace, where the pale princess lay on a high golden bed, barely breathing. The old man took the magic flower, crushed it in a teacup and let the princess drink the tea. The king, the ministers, ladies of the court, all stood by the bed holding their breath. In a moment colour returned to little princess' cheeks and she opened her eyes. The king was overjoyed. He took the old couple by the hand, gave them fine silken clothes and served them pickled tea with his own hands. "I thank you for giving my beloved daughter back to me. From this day on you are members of my family."

A few days afterwards, the king sat in the palace garden enjoying the evening cool. He called the old couple to sit with him and tell how they actually happened to get hold on the prince's jewel belt. The old man told the whole story, beginning from the day they rescued the tiger, the monkey, the snake and the boy Ko Maung from the river Irrawaddy. The old couple was still unaware of the whereabouts of their adopted son Ko Maung. They told the good king how worried they were because of the boy. The King of Pagan was a wise ruler and once he heard the story in full, he realised it was the ungrateful son Ko Maung who so viciously betrayed his good-hearted and simple rescuers. The king sent his soldiers to look for the traitor, and soon he was found gambling away the money he had received for double-crossing the old couple. The angry king wished to punish him severely, but the old woman still felt pity on him and pleaded on Ko Maung's behalf. Finally Ko Maung was sent into exile and warned never to return to the Golden Kingdom of Pagan.

The Burmese say that man is the most ungrateful creature walking on the face of the earth. Even a stray dog repays the scraps of food given to him by waking the household up in the night if a danger threatens them, but not the best hospitality and kindness is enough for a greedy and selfish person.

WHITE ELEPHANT AND THE HUNTER

Long ago there was a giant white elephant living peacefully with his herd in the deepest jungle. A hunting party happened to pass through the jungle in search of tigers. One of the hunters stopped to rest for a while and drink from a spring he saw between the rocks. The *nat* of the spring wanted to play a little trick on him, as the *nats* often do. When the hunter had drunk from the clearest and sweetest water, he fell asleep at once. After a while he woke up, but noticed that his party had gone and he was lost all alone in the jungle. The hunter was desperate! There were tigers and all kinds of other dangers lurking behind every rock and tree. And how could he survive the night? The sun was already setting. The hunter burst out crying aloud.

Suddenly he heard heavy steps coming in his direction. The bamboos and bushes were moved aside by a strong trunk and the hunter saw two black eyes on a huge face looking at him patiently. The hunter jumped up terrified! He knew that wild elephants protect their herd with all their awesome strength. And this one standing in front of him was the biggest elephant he had seen in his life. The huge animal was of silver colour and his tusks were almost touching the ground. With one step the mighty animal could have taken the hunter's life. But to the hunter's his great surprise, the white elephant spoke in a soft voice: "Don't be afraid, stranger. I am not going to hurt you. I heard your cry and came to look if I can help you." The hunter calmed down and told his story. The wise elephant understood that the forest *nats* had been playing their usual games with the poor man and he offered to protect him over night. "In the morning I will take you back to the Royal City, but you must promise not to tell the way to my herd to anyone. My family just wants to live in peace here in our jungle home." Of course the hunter promised everything, relieved to find safety against the dangers of the night. But in his dark mind a greedy idea began to grow.

In the morning the hunter came to the white elephant. "My saviour Mr. Elephant. I am a poor man and make my living by hunting. I don´t want to take life, but I have to do it for my family. If you give one of your shining white tusks, I will sell it to the king and live comfortably for the rest of my life." The white elephant had a good heart and he did hot hesitate a moment. He bent his majestic head so that the hunter could cut off one of his tusks. Then the elephant took the hunter to the Royal City gates. Before anyone could see, he disappeared back into the jungle.

The hunter sold the tusk for a good price, but he was a reckless man who liked gambling and drinking. The money was spent in one month. The hunter had got used to the easy life, so he took off to the jungle to look for the white elephant´s herd. He had taken notice of every turn of the road, so he found the elephant family quickly. The white elephant was surprised to see him, but welcomed him kindly anyway. The hunter knelt down in front of him: "Kind Mr. Elephant, have pity on me! My poor old mother became sick", he lied, since his mother and father had passed away years ago, "and I need more money for doctors and medicine!" The good-hearted white elephant bent his head at once to enable the greedy hunter to cut his other shining tusk. Again the elephant carried the hunter back to the Royal City gates, and disappeared into the jungle. And again the hunter ran to the gambling den where his drunken friends cheered him welcome. A month passed quickly and all the money was gone again.

One more time the ungrateful hunter walked through the jungle track to look for his gentle and good-hearted benefactor. This time he told a story, how his poor mother had died in spite of all the money spent on medicine and the best doctors. "Kind Mr. Elephant, you still have the roots of your tusks left. Let me please pull them out and sell them to the king's ivory carvers, so that I can give a proper funeral to my poor mother." On hearing these words from the evil and greedy hunter the jungle went silent. The chattering monkeys went quiet and even the little green parrots who cannot keep their beak shut for a minute, were still. But the kind white elephant did not hesitate. He knelt down to the ground in order to give a better chance to the hunter to pull the roots of his once handsome shining tusks out. And as he was planning to do so, a sudden green lightning struck in the middle of the jungle. Thagya Min, the King of *Deva Nats* was standing there in his golden and jewelled dress, shining like the burning rays of the midday sun. The hunter dropped down to his knees, frightened to see this celestial being in front of him. "How dare you, miserable hunter, abuse the unselfish charity of this royal animal!" blazed the voice of Thagya Min. The hunter hit his head on the ground mumbling his explanations, trying to pose as innocent and regretful. But you cannot fool Thagya Min who keeps a book on our good and bad deeds and sees everything from his throne up in Tavatimsa heaven. Before the hunter could say another word, the earth opened and swallowed him, and nothing was left of his wicked life. After that day the white elephant took his herd far away to the mountains and no one ever saw them near the Golden Kingdom again.

THE HERMIT AND THE KEINNAYEE

A thousand years ago in the city of Beikthano, there was a handsome and brave soldier in the king's army. After fighting wars and winning many victories he retired from the army and became a hermit, living alone on a far away secret mountain where men seldom wandered. Near his small monastery there was a cave. In it lived many happy *keinnaya* and *keinnayee*, who look like human beings except for their wings and feet, which are like birds' talons. The *keinnaya* and *keinnayee* are timid and shy creatures, and that is why very few people have ever seen them. The female *keinnayees* are full of beauty and grace. They fly out to dance and play with their husbands at dawn.

One dark night, when *Rahu* had swallowed the moon, a huge spider made his web at the entrance of the cave. In the morning, when the *keinnayas* flew out, one of them was caught in the sticky web. The spider, huge as a cartwheel, crawled to the sunlight and bit the poor helpless creature to death. In front of the horrified *keinnayas* the black monster drank the blood of his lifeless victim. The *keinnayas* and *keinnayees* did not know what to do. This cave was their home, but every morning and evening one of them was caught by the evil spider. One of them remembered that their hermit neighbour had once been a famous warrior in the king's army. So they decided to ask their friend for help.

The *keinnayas* sent a delegation to talk with the hermit. "Venerable neighbour. Our families are facing a terrible threat every morning and evening. An evil black monster, huge in size and invincible in strength is killing our husbands and wives. You are a wise and virtuous man. Please help us!" The hermit scolded them saying: "I am a hermit. I have made a solemn promise not to take life of others, human or animal. How dare you ask me to break my vows." And he sent them away. The distraught *keinnayas* went back to their cave to think of another plan to solve their problem. Among the *keinnayees* was a young and very beautiful maid called Yatawaddy. She came forward with a perfect idea.

Next morning the *keinnayees* dressed Yatawaddy in a golden dress and jewels. They decorated her shining black hair with sweet smelling jasmine and orchids. On her slender soft fingers she wore precious ruby rings. Dressed like this, she looked exactly like a *deva nat* fallen down from heaven. Another delegation flew to the hermit's monastery, carrying many kinds of valuable presents with them. Beautiful Yatawaddy followed last with downcast eyes. The hermit saw the delegation and was about to send them away with angry words, but on seeing Yatawaddy, who shone like a celestial being, his words got lost on the way. The head *keinnaya* of the delegation begged the hermit to help them and to become their king with Yatawaddy as his wife. The hermit fell in love with Yatawaddy, who also had secretly looked at the handsome hermit and felt the same. And so an agreement was made. The hermit would fight the huge spider in exchange for Yatawaddy.

Next morning the hermit was up with the sun. He went to the cave with a hammer in his hand. He shook the sticky web as if there was a victim caught in it, and when the nasty-looking spider came out to look for his food, he killed it with one strong stoke. Then he broke the web and the keinnayas were again free to fly as they wished.

The *keinnayee* Yatawaddy married the hermit, and they lived happily on the secret mountain until they died at a very old age. I believe their great grandchildren still live there today.

RABBIT AS A FORTUNE TELLER

In the forest near the holy city of Sagaing lived a clever and kind-hearted rabbit. Whenever other animals of the forest needed advice, they always found their way to the humble grass hut of the rabbit. The rabbit always helped.

One lazy afternoon a tiger happened to come by. He was hungry and therefore looking for a reason to quarrel with others. Other animals disappeared into the bushes but rabbit continued scratching his fur in peace.

"So you are the famous rabbit of this forest. Other animals tell me you are clever and can see their fortune. How about you yourself? Can you see the day you die?" asked the grumpy tiger. "Certainly I can see my own future as well as others. One day I will die of hunger" answered the rabbit lifting his brown eyes to face the tiger. "A-aa… and what day will it be?" grimaced the tiger, since he had a plan to have a nice fat rabbit roast that very same afternoon. "Well let me check now," said the rabbit closing his eyes and pretending to meditate, "it will be exactly one day before you die."

Tigers are very superstitious and from that day on, he did not fail to visit rabbit's grass hut every day and bring many kinds of eatables for him. The rabbit lived a long and peaceful life under the protection of the huge tiger. And when he finally died, the tiger got so scared that he too dropped dead.

HUNTER SAVES THE VILLAGE

Long ago there lived a young and handsome hunter called Ko Nyi in the village near the river Sittaung. He earned a living by hunting wild boar in the jungle. It was tough and dangerous work, but Ko Nyi went on climbing the mountains and brought his catch to the village market. One morning, after a very heavy storm that had even uprooted huge jungle trees from their age-old roots, Ko Nyi was walking his trail when he heard weeping under the crushed branches of a fig tree. Being a gentle and kind person Ko Nyi lifted the branches, only to find two green parrots with broken wings. Feeling pity on the poor birds he took them to his hut, gave them water and fruit and bound their wings with medicinal herbs. Many people who live close with nature know about various plants, leaves and flowers that can cure different illnesses. But even an experienced hunter like Ko Nyi did not know that birds could speak human language if only they want to.

After a few days in the tender care of Ko Nyi the parrots recovered. When they tried their wings and noticed that they were strong enough, the male parrot opened his bright yellow beak and said: "Ko Nyi, me and my wife owe our life to you. To show our gratitude, we give you the gift of understanding the language of all creatures. But you must promise never to tell anybody that you have this skill. If you do, you will be turned at once into a wooden statue."

The astonished Ko Nyi swore to keep the promise as long as he lived. The female bird then flew on his right shoulder and the male bird sat on his left shoulder. Both of them whispered some magic syllables in his ears and then flew back to the jungle.

That day changed the life of Ko Nyi. He could hear the babble of the monkeys about who found the new fruit trees and understood how the deer mother taught her little ones how to escape from the tiger. He talked with the king of the jungle, the white elephant, and saw that even the snake took care of its children. He began to feel so much compassion for the life of the animals he hunted that could no longer raise his hand against even one of them. Instead he collected fruit and wild vegetables for sale in the village market. One day he overheard two eagles talking about a fierce storm arising on the horizon. Ko Nyi climbed quickly to the highest top of the mountain and sharpened his eyes all he could. No, all he could see was the smiling sun and gentle winds driving tiny white clouds in the blue skies. When he noticed that many animals were taking cover and all the birds were flying away, he became very alarmed. He had to warn the villagers, many of whom were his good friends.

Ko Nyi ran down the mountain slope as fast as he could. He rushed to the village just in good time for dinner, when the farmers were returning from their fields in the bullocks. Ko Nyi ran to the headman's house. He was so out of breath that everybody laughed. And when he told them to pack quickly everything valuable and leave as fast as they could, they laughed even more. "Hunter has been sleeping under the sun and now he thinks the village is on fire!" they shouted. "Look, a perfect evening. The sun is about to go down and the sky is like ruby and gold. Don't worry hunter. Come and have dinner with us." But Ko Nyi did not give up. He tried to convince them and pushed them away when they tried to calm him down. Many of the villagers even thought he had gone crazy, living alone up in his mountain hut.

Finally, when Ko Nyi realised that no one was going to believe him and that the village would be destroyed, he decided to tell his story no matter what. He collected all the villagers around him and began. When he told how he found the two parrots, his feet started to feel heavy. In the part where the birds speak in human language, his lower body turned wooden and when the story was at an end, his face became motionless. His left arm was pointing towards the road out from the village. Ko Nyi had turned into a wooden statue. Now the villagers realised he had not lied or become crazy. They ran quickly to their houses, packed what they could and left the village for safety. When the last bullock left the village gate it started to rain. It rained and stormed the whole night. All the houses in the village were destroyed but thanks to brave and unselfish Ko Nyi not even a cat of the village was harmed.

When the villagers returned the next day, they were very quiet. They built their houses and cleaned their gardens. But the statue of Ko Nyi pointing to saving them they carried to the gate of the village, where every passer-by paid him their respects every day. When you pass an old village in the Burmese countryside, you may see that he stands there, guarding the safety of the village even today.

LITTLE RABBIT HAS A RUNNING NOSE

The lion king of the jungle had a problem. He had a huge hole between his two back teeth. Whenever he ate, something always got stuck there. And as the lions like to eat meat, his breath became awfully smelly. Animal kings are like their human counterparts – they need ministers to serve and keep them in good mood.

Lion king had three ministers, a strong and sturdy boar, a talkative monkey and a clever little rabbit. One day the lion was annoyed, for his tooth was aching and further, because his lion queens turned their heads away when he came close to them. A he asked his ministers, "What is the matter tell me honestly, or bear the consequences."

First it was the boar's turn. He shook his big head, embarrassed, and finally said: "My Lord, maybe it is the foul smell coming from Your Majesty's mouth that makes the queens turn away." RRRROAR… and the poor minister boar was on his way towards the belly of the lion.

Next morning the lion king's tooth was aching even more, and since he had eaten one of his ministers, his mouth was even smellier. He summoned the monkey and very annoyed asked: "What is the matter?" Tell me honestly why my queens do not love me anymore, or bear the consequences." The monkey had seen what happened to the boar, but he did not dare to lie. He shook his long tail, embarrassed, and said finally: "My Lord, maybe it is the foul smell com-

ing from Your Majesty's mouth that makes the queens turn away."
RRRROAR... and the poor minister monkey was on his way towards the belly of the lion.

On the third morning lion king woke up with a terrible pain in his tooth. To his great anger not even one of his queens came to greet him. So he was furious when ordering minister rabbit in front of him. "What is the matter" he roared in pain at his last minister, "is my mouth smelly and awful. Tell me honestly, or bear the consequences."

The rabbit bowed his head respectfully in front of the king and said: "Your Majesty, I do not smell anything for I have a running nose." Then he quickly took a bamboo stick, opened the lion's mouth and fished out a huge rotten bone from between his teeth. The pain was relieved at once, and the lion king rewarded his clever minister in many ways and kept him always close for good advice.

This story explains why the Burmese, when they do not wish to tell the truth if it could embarrass the other person, say that the little rabbit has a running nose.

MANOUKTHIHA

Once upon time, there lived a huge lion in the forested hills behind the Royal City of Mandalay. He was the undisputed king of the wilderness. People knew him by his royal name Manoukthiha and by his roar, which could be heard when the full moon rose above the hills.

Manoukthiha had been practising magic under the guidance of a famous *zawgyi* when he was young. He had a tender heart and he longed for the company of a loving female. One hot day, the minor queens of the Mandalay court had been sent to gather sweet-smelling flowers for the king's delight. The minor queens were happy to have a good reason for a nice picnic. Life in the royal court can be very boring despite all the luxury. Minor queens seldom saw the ruler of their life and destiny, and many had to suffer the jealousy of the main queens if they happened to be pretty. So a day in the forest was welcomed and the ladies were chatting and laughing happily as the bullocks pulled them away from their golden cage.

One of the minor queens was a sweet little thing. Her name was Hla Hla, meaning very beautiful. She joined the party singing with the other ladies. When they reached the hillside, the ladies took their baskets and scattered among the flowers like colourful butterflies. Hla Hla wandered a little further into the forest, picking flowers and humming a happy melody. Finally she looked up, but could not see the others anymore. She became worried and shouted the names of the other ladies. Nobody answered. Manoukthiha heard her cries in his cave. He decided to come and see what was the matter, for he too, like all men, weakened at womens´ tears.

Manoukthiha came closer to the place where poor Hla Hla was crying her eyes out. "What a beautiful little thing", he thought, "if I only could win her heart to love me, I would never have to feel lonely." He knew that she would die of fear if he just jumped out from the bushes in his lion form. So he uttered magic words that the famous *zawgyi* had taught him long ago, and transformed himself into a handsome young man in shining golden armour.

When Hla Hla lifted her eyes, a surprising and most welcome sight met her. Manoukthiha spoke soft words of love to her and made her forget all about the king in Mandalay Palace. She promised to follow him to his forest home (which, with more magic, Manoukthiha had made to look like a fine palace) and became his wife. So they lived happily together. When Manoukthiha was with his wife he took his human form. Otherwise he roamed the forests in his lion form.

Manuokthiha and his wife had a son, who grew up in the magic palace unaware of his father´s true being. When he was twenty years old, he started to wonder what the world would be like outside the forest. His parents warned him not to leave the hillsides, but since when have sons listened to their fathers?

One day, when his mother was cooking a tasty dinner and his father was on his way, the young man could not resist the temptation. He decided to go and see for himself what the world was like, find the adventures and excitement beyond the familiar hills. He sneaked out and ran down the little path on which his father had led up his mother twenty years ago. He saw the shining golden pagodas and towers of distant Mandalay ahead, and he ran even faster.

Suddenly he noticed a huge lion following him. It was his father Manoukthiha, but of course the son did not recognise him in his lion form. The son had inherited his father's fearless nature. Without a moment's hesitation he picked a strong and straight bamboo and pierced his father's heart with it. As soon as the warm blood gushed out, the lion Manoukthiha changed once more into a man.

The son was desperate. He cried and cried, holding his beloved father's head in his lap. Next morning be buried the body, took his worried mother from the cave palace, which had now turned into an ordinary cave, and continued his journey to the king's city. In Mandalay, he joined the king's army and made a career as an outstanding and brave officer.

When he had collected a large enough fortune, he retired and ordered a huge sculpture from the best artists in Mandalay in honour of his wise and good-hearted father, who had given him life and who had tried to protect him. The sculpture had a human head attached to a lion's body. When you visit Mandalay, you can still find this sculpture standing near the big pagoda.

THE MONKEY AND THE CROCODILE

A clever little monkey lived happily in the forest. He was very fond of juicy fresh mangoes. One day he saw from the tallest tree-top a bountiful mango orchard growing on a tiny island on the other side of the river. He ran quickly to the riverside and wondered how to get to the other side. Monkeys you see, really hate swimming. After a while the clever little monkey found a place where big stones led over the river. There he could pass over to the mango orchard without getting his paws wet.

Every morning the clever little monkey jumped over the river, and every evening he came back with his belly full. In the river there also lived also two crocodiles, an old couple. The female crocodile began to imagine a tasty monkey roast and she told her husband: "Go and catch me that tasty looking monkey. He has been eating mangoes all day, and he will certainly make a nice evening meal for us."

The male crocodile could not refuse his wife's wishes and so he went, hiding in the river. Only the top of his head was visible. It looked exactly like a stone. Crocodiles are very patient, and this one lay without moving the whole day. In the evening the monkey returned from the mango orchard back to the riverside. He was just about to jump on to the stones leading over the river, when he noticed there was one extra stone there. The clever little monkey smelled something fishy. So he shouted with a loud voice: "Good evening my old friend Mr. Stone! How was your day?"

The crocodile was a little alarmed. He had never ever in his long life heard a stone speaking, but since the monkey was obviously an old friend with the stone, maybe it did talk anyway. He thought the monkey would be suspicious if the stone did not answer, and so he replied: "I am fine my friend!" Now the clever little monkey knew there was no safe trip home.

"Ah, it is you, Mr. Crocodile. What are you hiding there for, behind the stones?" The crocodile was embarrassed to see he was found out so easily. "I am not hiding, " he answered, "I am here to catch a monkey roast for my lovely wife." "Well, that would be me," said the clever little monkey politely. "If you open your mouth wide, I will jump right into it." "That is mighty decent of you" replied the crocodile contentedly. This hunt seemed to be going much better than he had thought at the start.

The crocodile opened his jaws as wide as he could. At that very moment the clever little monkey jumped over the stones and on the top of the crocodile's head to the safe side of the river. Crocodiles, you see, always close their eyes when they open their mouth.

RABBIT´S PICTURE IN THE MOON

Once upon a time there was a wise rabbit living in the forest with his good friends the monkey, the fox and the otter. The other animals respected the rabbit for his virtues of charity and learning. They always followed his good advice.

It was the time for *Thadingyut*, the festival of lights, and people were travelling to famous pagodas for meditation and festivities. The rabbit advised that the four animals should collect food for donation. "It is always good to prepare for charity and hospitality", he said, "and a special festival day gives us an opportunity to share our well-being with others who may not be so fortunate." The monkey, the fox and the otter agreed and went back to their forest homes. The King of the *Deva Nats* Thagya Min, who keeps a book on our good merit, happened to hear the rabbit´s words. He decided to check how the animals were succeeding in their plan.

The monkey climbed fruit trees. He picked the best and juiciest papayas, mangoes and bananas, and took them to his home tree. The fox ran to the outskirts of the village. He dug in the rubbish dump for the tasty rotten chicken bones and fish heads that the foxes love so much. And he took his catch to his home cave in the forest. The otter swam in the river and collected plenty of mussels and small fish. All of them he took to his sandy home hole by the riverbank.

All the three animals kept a fast for the evening in order to donate the food next day to visitors and passers-by. But the rabbit, who gave such a good advice to the other animals, made a little nest from dry grass and slept happily the whole night.

In the morning the monkey, the fox and the otter took their food donations out and waited for someone to walk by the forest path on his way to the small white pagoda on the hilltop. But nobody came. When it was close to noon, the monkey saw a wandering hermit dressed in a dark brown robe and a high brown hat walking along the path. The monkey offered his fruit to the hermit, who of course was Thagya Min in disguise. The hermit took some and blessed his host for the virtues of charity and hospitality.

The fox also offered his favourite smelly foods to the hermit. The hermit took some and blessed his host for the virtues of charity and hospitality. The otter had brought all the mussels and little fish he had caught the day before in the river. He offered them to the hermit who took some and blessed his host for the virtues of charity and hospitality.

Lastly the hermit came to the rabbit. The rabbit was taking a nap in the shadow of a big stone. The hermit woke him up and told him he had walked a long way to attend the pagoda festival. He asked if the rabbit could offer him a little food. The rabbit did not have any-thing, because rabbits just eat grass whereever they find it and never keep a store. But the wise rabbit did not hesitate: "Honoured guest, please sit down here in the shadow and rest a while. I will quickly cook you a nice meal." Then he disappeared behind the stone.

The rabbit gathered a bunch of dry wood and grass to make a fire. He waited until the flames were high. The hermit listened to the noise and asked: "What is going on, my host? I smell smoke." "Nothing to worry about, dear guest. I will be ready soon with your meal!" the rabbit answered, and then he jumped into the flames. He wanted to offer the hermit a meal, and since he did not have anything he planned to cook himself.

The rabbit was sitting in the burning fire, but the flames did not touch him! It was not even hot even though he tried to roll in the fire. Not one hair of his fur was even singed. The hermit came over to the rabbit, who sat there surprised. The hermit assumed his real shining form as the King of the *Deva Nats*. With a wave of his hand he made the fire fade. Thagya Min took the scared little rabbit gently in his hands and praised his bravery and unselfishness. Surely this offering was the greatest charity and hospitality of all. In honour of the rabbit, Thagya Min drew the rabbit's picture on the moon to remind us that we should be ready to sacrifice ourselves for other living beings.

If you look carefully at the full moon on a clear night, you can see the rabbit's picture there still today.